Sustaining Your Spirituality

Sally Nash

Director of the Midlands Centre for Youth Ministry,
a partnership between St John's Nottingham and Youth for Christ

GROVE BOOKS LIMITED
RIDLEY HALL RD CAMBRIDGE CB3 9HU

Contents

Acknowledgments

Although I am the author of this booklet, the content draws on the ministry of both Paul and myself and the ideas and examples reflect our work both separately and together. For that reason I usually use the terms 'we' and 'our' in the booklet. For most of our twenty or so years together we have worked for the same organization, initially Youth for Christ and now the Midlands Centre for Youth Ministry, although Paul's main job now is as Senior Chaplain at Birmingham Children's Hospital. Much of our church-based ministry is as a couple. I would also like to thank staff and volunteers in Youth for Christ and Centre for Youth Ministry students who have contributed so much to this booklet as we have explored together many of the issues and concepts covered.

The Cover Illustration is a photograph by Paul Nash

First Impression March 2006
ISSN 1748-3492
ISBN 1 85174 618 8

Introduction

I'm fed up! I feel like giving up.
I can't do this anymore, I can't keep it up.
What is it that I can do to nourish and sustain my relationship with God?
Where is sacred space for me?
What renews and restores me?
If the most important thing is my relationship with God, how come I
don't give it more time?
I want a life as well as a job or a ministry—how do I do it?

We have heard statements and questions like these many times over the 20 or so years that our work has involved training and supporting youth workers. Through our own journey and that of others, we have discovered some of the answers and I am sharing them here in the hope that others can find a spirituality that sustains long-term involvement in ministry, whether that is full-time or a session or two a week.

There is no 'youth' in the title of this book because in essence I believe that the resources which are helpful for sustaining youth ministry are the same as the resources needed for sustaining any ministry, indeed that are helpful for sustaining our own spirituality whatever it is we do. However, I believe that it is an important contribution to the Youth Series because of the high demands that being a youth worker—volunteer or full-time—makes of us.

My experience is that to sustain a ministry that is rooted in a real, living relationship with God is not always easy and requires self-knowledge, reflection, support from other people, time to find a pattern or rhythm that works and a willingness to persevere through the hard times.

To sustain a ministry that is rooted in a real, living relationship with God is not always easy

This booklet seeks to help us identify what it is we already do that helps sustain us and to explore, perhaps outside our current experience and heritage, ways in which we can sustain our spirituality. It is important to be honest with ourselves, to face our fears, questions, doubts and weaknesses as well as our strengths, joys and encouragements. There is an increasing trend for various types of self-examination of our bodies—should we not do the same with our spirits? Human beings are spiritual beings and if God is essentially Spirit then this is how we communicate with God, spirit to Spirit.

It is also important to make clear that the answers to the questions above may not always be overtly 'spiritual.' When asked 'What sustains your spirituality?' answers from a group of experienced workers included:

- taking photos or painting
- spending half a day in a cathedral (and then making good use of the coffee shop!) or a silent retreat
- having a bath for as long as it takes to resolve an issue
- a long walk along the sands watching the tide go in and out
- reading a light novel to switch off completely
- baking and sharing the results!
- sacred space website[1]
- going to the gym
- swimming lengths reflecting on the Psalms or the Ten Commandments

The important thing is to resist the temptation to have stereotypical ideas about the 'right' way to sustain spirituality

These are just suggestions. The important thing is to work out what is helpful for us and to resist the temptation to have stereotypical ideas about the 'right' way to sustain spirituality.

However, I am not saying that tried and tested ways of sustaining our spirituality are no longer important or relevant. I still enjoy a liturgical morning prayer, albeit Celtic. Paul reads a chapter of the Bible daily and does this having been inspired by a story he heard:

An elderly man was asked why he still read his Bible every day. Did he forget what he read? Didn't he know all the stories by now? He replied that every day for the past 36 years he had eaten a meal cooked by his wife. He couldn't remember what he ate last month but the fact that he was still healthy and fit suggested that he had eaten well. He couldn't say on a daily basis what reading the Bible had achieved, but he knew that he still loved God and was aware that he had not been alone during the ups and downs of his life.

Fortunately, Paul has not fully taken the story on board and does do his share of the cooking!

Why Can it be Difficult to Sustain a Strong Relationship with God?

Some of the issues discussed in this section may apply more to people in recognised ministry, but for most of us there are times when it is difficult to sustain our relationship with God. Identifying some of the reasons for this may enable us to put into place things that help.

1 Meeting the young peoples' needs at the expense of our own
Most people in youth work are there because they are passionately committed to young people and want to do the best for them. With the many needs that some young people have and often a lack of resources within our youth work, we can feel a pressure to take on too much and may not leave enough time to ensure that our own needs are being met. This is a road that leads to excessive stress and burnout and both we and the young people suffer if things get to this stage.

Finding a holistic spirituality that sustains can be part of the solution to this problem. We have also discovered that finding a group or place that feels like home spiritually, outside of where we are ministering, helps to refresh and renew us. For some this is found in relationship to a monastic or other form of community, for others it may be a small group of like-minded people in ministry. We all need places where we are nourished so we can continue to minister to others.

2 Buying into a culture of production and success
It is not difficult to believe that who we are is inextricably tied up with what we do and to get our identity primarily from our work, whether paid or voluntary. This means that we can get so busy that we neglect to spend time just being and our inner life remains unnourished. We explore this further in Chapter 3.

3 Feeling that our relationship with God has become work
When we are in ministry it can feel like spending time with God is just another part of the job and that we need to tick that task off the list, along with planning the youth group, meeting up with a young person for a mentoring session and writing a report for the church leadership. It can be hard to break out of that mindset but finding a way of spending time with God or nourishing our spiritual being that does not seem like work can be a good idea. In a mini-research project on devotional times carried out by Midlands Centre for Youth Ministry students, engaging with nature was the most popular way of spending time with God, a way of connecting to God that encourages restoration and recreation.

4 Fear of what happens when you get close to God

It is possible to fear what God might say if we get too close to him and allow our busyness to become a substitute for intimacy with God and a more holistic relationship that shapes every part of our lives. This can particularly be true when we are avoiding dealing with an issue or area of life which we know is not quite right, or if we feel that God has let us down in the past and we are afraid of being vulnerable again.

We both still have a little bit of the old evangelical legacy of 'if you don't want to do it, it must be God!' Paul jokes that he used to pray, 'Lord, whatever I have done wrong, I repent now, but please don't make me be a vicar!' Becoming an ordained Anglican was the right move for him, although God was gracious and let him be a hospital chaplain, which enables him to combine his passions for mission and pastoral care in a place where someone else looks after the buildings!

5 Lack of exposure to or experience of approaches to spirituality

Sometimes we have not found out what works for us or explored how best to nourish ourselves spiritually. A spiritual director, soul friend, accompanier, mentor (whichever term we prefer) may be able to help us find ways of connecting with God that work for us. Looking out for ways of broadening our understanding of spirituality can be good. I did a 'praying with colour' course a couple of years ago and this has opened up new ways of exploring my inner life.

Walking by the sea is one of our most restorative activities—just a shame we live in Birmingham! But regular breaks where we do get to do this have helped us be in ministry for over 20 years and to thrive rather than perish in that environment, because we have had space free from pressure to process things and regain perspective if that is what we need.

Something else that has been helpful has been to explore our Christian heritage. In his training for ministry Paul was on placement in a high Anglican, black majority church. He found he envied their sense of rootedness and this led to an exploration of Celtic Christianity and examining those roots. The value of stability in Benedictine spirituality has been valuable in helping me to work through staying for over twenty years in Youth for Christ, when many of my contemporaries moved on long ago, and in a culture which talks about having several careers over a lifetime of work. What could be perceived as boring and unadventurous takes on a different dimension when viewed as a response to God's call to stability.

What could be perceived as boring and unadventurous takes on a different dimension when viewed as a response to God's call to stability

6 Unhelpful images of God or ministry
There is a tendency in contemporary culture to compartmentalize our lives and live consistently *in* different areas but not *between* them—a dualistic approach. Seeking to live an integrated life where God is acknowledged in all areas can help us face issues that might be keeping us away from God. Spending some time reflecting on our past can be helpful too as we seek to identify what has caused these wrong images. I can be driven by 'oughts' and sometimes take on things because I feel I ought to, rather than because I genuinely believe God wants me to do them. Sometimes we do just need to get on and serve, but at other times our service can almost be negated by the unhelpful baggage we bring with us, because we have not worked through some of the things in our past.

7 Being in the work for the wrong reason
Guilt, ambition, apathy, staying safe or lack of belief in our ability can all be reasons for staying in a job or role that drains us. In such circumstances spending time with God becomes difficult because we find it hard to see how our pain can be transformed. This can apply if we feel trapped in a particular role as a volunteer too and we can begin to feel resentful because of it.

Questions for Reflection

- Which of these reasons do you relate to?
- Are there any others you can identify?

Spending some time reflecting on how and why we have difficulty in sustaining our relationship with God in the midst of ministry and life can help us identify issues we need to engage with or deal with, as we seek to continue our journey of becoming more like Christ.

In the rest of this booklet I want to explore three areas that seem useful in developing a spirituality that sustains. These ideas have been developed from research and experience and have been used in all sorts of contexts: with full-time youth workers; for an inner city church Lent Course; with students and volunteer youth workers; hospital chaplaincy; and to help people with their daily life and work. The first area considers using images and metaphors to explore our spirituality and help identify what sustains us. The second area involves spiritual exercises that help us discern, understand ourselves and make decisions, choosing what brings us life. The third is the idea of marker posts and shelters, a rule and rhythm that helps us develop a pattern to sustain our spiritual lives and ministry. Underpinning all these areas is the idea and importance of seeing and encountering God in the everyday—living an integrated life.

2   Images and Metaphors for Sustaining Spirituality

Images and metaphors often help us to go deeper, to explore the different layers or aspects of a situation.

We have found a variety of images and metaphors helpful at different stages of the journey. The important thing is to find one that works for us, that brings new insights into our spiritual lives. In this chapter I explore two in depth, both of which emerged from our research with youth workers—the 'mixer desk' from Paul's work and 'fruitfulness' from mine. I then suggest other images and metaphors that may be helpful or inspire further reflection.

What has a Mixer Desk got to do with Sustaining Spirituality?

Mixer desks are a common sight in youth work, where young people get to be DJs and mix different sounds together. It is a helpful image in exploring resources for sustaining spirituality, as we can see it as an image of our lives and look at how different elements contribute or distract from what it is we want to do or be. The great thing about a mixer desk is that it is not static. The way it is set up changes and that is what our spirituality is like—it evolves and develops as we change, mature and reflect on who we are and where we are going.

It evolves and develops as we change, mature and reflect on who we are and where we are going

The core questions to be asked when using this metaphor are:

> - How is your mixer desk set up?
> - What are the elements in your life that contribute to your unique 'sound'?

Before we begin to set up our mixer desk we need to have some idea of what sort of 'music' we want to make. In terms of this metaphor, the 'music,' for us, relates to our calling and the first step involves working out what God is calling us to.[2] When we begin to grasp this we can start putting into place things (practices, people, choices, training and so on) that will help us fulfil that

Understanding and articulating our calling may well be fundamental to our ability to sustain ministry long-term

vision. Our calling can underpin everything else in sustaining our ministry. We have heard people say many times that it is only the sense of being called that keeps them going in a difficult place. Understanding and articulating our calling may well be fundamental to our ability to sustain ministry long-term whether this is full-time or as a volunteer.

When we have done this exercise, what has emerged for us is that the 'music' has changed a little over the years but tends to involve some elements of education, equipping and empowering (for me), and equipping, mission, pastoring and encouraging (for Paul), depending on the context where we are playing our 'music.' Our mixer desks are set up to help us fulfil these callings in the long term. We need a spirituality that sustains us to be able to build God's kingdom in the way that he has called us to.

There are various different ways of exploring calling. Agnes Sanford coined the phrase 'sealed orders,'[3] envisaging a conversation between us and God before we are born, which talks about what our unique purpose on earth will be, which then unfolds throughout our life. The biblical roots of this may well be Ephesians 2:10 'For we are God's workmanship, created in Christ Jesus to do good works, which God prepared in advance for us to do.' Reflecting on our lives and the things we enjoy, that are significant to us (if not to others) and that make us feel fulfilled, may help us uncover more of what we understand our calling to be, as can reviewing what God has said to us over the years.

What do you think your sealed orders are?
Eudaimonia is an ancient Greek term that can be translated as the feeling you get when you act in a way that is true to yourself. *'Daimon'* is a state of excellence which you work towards to give your life meaning. *Eudaimonia* is thus being able to be who you really are, realizing your potential, becoming all God created you to be.[4] This is related to John 10:10 — 'life in all its fullness.'

'Daimon' is a state of excellence which you work towards to give your life meaning

What is it in your life that makes you feel like this?
Another way of looking at this is to think about your fundamental calling. What underpins all you do? Think about all the different ways you have served God and look for the common themes, patterns and foundations that emerge.

Questions for Reflection

- What ministry or work with young people makes you feel excited?
- What gives you a deep inner joy?
- What needs in the world most concern you?
- What would you like to be remembered for?

Looking at these concepts, can you find a way to express your calling, your mission?

Having worked out your calling or vision—the 'music'—it is then time to look at how the mixer desk is set up and whether changes are necessary. Consider what 'sounds' can be heard and the balance of those sounds that you are 'listening' to. The sounds may be all those elements usually involved in life and ministry and could include, as well as your calling and vision, things such as self-knowledge, faith/spiritual tradition, expectations from self and others, young people and church, demands of the job, other responsibilities and roles, hopes and dreams, and so on.

For us, an important part of our mixer desk, almost a very loud bass track, is a regular pattern of time away and retreat. We put in a retreat and regular time off at the beginning of the year, as soon as we know our main commitments, so we know that the pace of life is one we can manage and that there are regular opportunities for recharging and refreshment. Because we are both busy and can work irregular hours, one of the things we have had to do is to have clear expectations of each other and that is a sound that needs to be very loud. We both have other responsibilities and roles that are important to us and these factor into our mixer desk—Paul is ordained and I am a lay leader in the Church of England and we both think it is important to work out these roles in our local church. For us, taking a service once a month is the right balance, it is the right set-up for us. Another element that is important for me is a monthly commitment to praying with a friend, something that has been in the diary for fifteen years or so. For Paul there is the area of community service where he is on the committee of a local hostel. Other key sounds for us are hospitality, quiet times (very different from each other—one in the morning and the other in the evening), regular walks, seeing people in ministry to offer support, and seeing our spiritual directors. All these elements help to sustain our spirituality and thus help us be more effective in the ministry God has called us to. We have also needed to look at what might be missing or discordant and at various times have sought to address these by altering the set up of the way we live our lives. Different seasons have led to different set-ups.

All these elements help us to be more effective in the ministry God has called us to

Having looked at the way your mixer desk is set up now, try looking at the different elements or sounds and reflect on:

- Which sounds are loudest? Are they the right ones?
- Which sounds have been minimized? Whose voice or perspective hasn't been heard properly? Who or what is being drowned out?
- Are there any missing sounds? Is there something that needs to be added?
- Is there something out of sync? Are there discordant notes?
- Where is the bass line? What underpins your life?
- What else are you hearing or not hearing?
- Are there changes that you need to make?

Fruitfulness

- Who have you not thanked for their contribution to your past life?
- Who would be really surprised to see you where you are now?
- Who might be wondering how you turned out?

So often the people who have influenced us do not know the impact they have had. They do not know to what extent that aspect of their ministry was 'successful.' That is one of the difficulties with youth work—how do we measure success? We live and work in an environment where success or performance is often measured in terms of how much, how many, how far, how, how often. This approach does not always work for those involved in youth ministry. However, to be able to sustain our ministry, most of us need to have some idea of how we are getting on. Fruitfulness is a way of exploring this that stays true to a biblical image and gives us a way of evaluating what we do. Psalm 1:3 uses this metaphor, describing the person who is blessed as being 'like a tree planted by streams of water, which yields its fruit in season.'

To be able to sustain our ministry, most of us need to have some idea of how we are getting on

A metaphor is a helpful way of looking at things but the metaphor should not be taken to its extremes. Otherwise, in this case, it may lead to heated discussions as to what variety of 'fruit' is the best! Is it the fruit that preaches to a thousand young people or the one that stays up until the early hours listening to a young person whose father has just walked out of home? Whether your favourite story about Jesus is the feeding of the five thousand or the parable of the lost sheep may influence what you think is the most effective or important ministry. Nouwen brings insight to the difference between success and fruitfulness:

> There is a great difference between successfulness and fruitfulness. Success comes from strength, control and respectability…Fruits, however, come from weakness and vulnerability. And fruits are unique.[5]

Acknowledging this as our starting place in ministry reinforces our dependence on God. It is also interesting to think about the uniqueness of pieces of fruit and to be able to acknowledge that we have made a contribution that only we could have made—others would have done it another way with perhaps different outcomes.

All sorts of words may come to mind when we think of fruitfulness. Here are a few of them—success, flourishing, fit, growing, good reputation, servant-hearted, credibility, authority, faithfulness, powerful, vitality, commitment, longevity, creative, innovative, accountable.

- Which ones resonate with you?
- Which others would you add?
- What does fruitfulness mean to you?

To explore what fruitfulness in ministry means, it is necessary to consider what ministry is. Literally, the word means service. My personal theology is rooted in Philippians 2:5–11 and the concept of having the same attitude as Christ Jesus. This means, for me, that fruitfulness is about service, humility, vulnerability, relinquishment and obedience. These are values, attitudes and attributes that I seek (but sometimes fail!) to have in my ministry.

What fruitfulness means for us will depend on how we see ministry and what God has called us to. We have heard youth workers talk of such things as compassion for those they work with, an ability to let young people be autonomous, living with the grey areas of ambiguity, having a positive self-perception of their role and contribution, holding on to hope when faced with the seemingly hopeless, feeling more love and other fruit of the Spirit towards those they work with (particularly colleagues) and few regrets or 'if only's.

However, over the years we have realized that to be fruitful in ministry certain conditions are needed, just as natural fruit needs the right soil, water and sunshine to develop and ripen.[6] Research amongst youth workers[7] suggests that the following are some of the things that help them be fruitful.

Personal Context:

- Spiritual lives rooted in a knowledge and love of God, self and others that demonstrate faithfulness, obedience, and spiritual disciplines supported by a spiritual director or equivalent.

- Understanding ministry as serving and servanthood and preferring the needs of others, in imitation of Christ.

- Good stewardship of time, resources, gifts and abilities.

- Being released into ministry by those close to and committed to them.

- Knowing what refreshes, restores and re-envisions them and making that a regular part of life-space just for 'me.'

Work Context:

- Working relationships where they have a sense of belonging, are part of a team and look out for others and are looked out for.

- Mentoring and development for themselves and from them to others.

- Mary/Martha balance of being and doing, including basic needs such as food, exercise, sleep, time off, time out somewhere different, holidays, retreats, hobbies and social life.

- Good management with a clear vision, realistic expectations, reasonable conditions of service, appropriate supervision and encouragement.

- Sounding-board/non-managerial supervision and the opportunity to get perspectives from outside the situation.

- Adequate time to spend with God that is seen as an integral part of being in ministry as well as a personal responsibility. For example, paid retreats.

- What are the equivalents for you?
- What of the above resonates?
- What would you add or take away?

If you are a volunteer in youth ministry, it may be helpful to see how some of these principles can be built into your own life. Having times of supervision, training, development, reflection and retreat are important for volunteers as well as full-timers, and this will often have a knock-on effect on the work, as you have time and space to think about what you are doing. Many churches find that it works best to use the time that a group usually meets for these sorts of activities, for example, having a leader's meeting on the first week of a new term with the young people returning on the second week. Perhaps a commitment to one Saturday or Sunday a year for some longer input could also be considered. Thinking holistically about what helps you to be fruitful in all areas of your life as well as your youth work might be a good task for a quiet day or half day or could even be a team exercise.

Healthy Eating or Diet

My New Year's resolutions for as many years as I can remember have contained one about losing weight. For the first year ever probably this year I am building on weight loss from the previous year. What made the difference? I found a pattern that worked for me that enabled me to lose weight and then sustain that weight loss over six months. The approach combined a change of perspective—focusing on eating healthily rather than the deprivation and loss associated with many other diet attempts—with a flexible structure that built in days off, holidays and other special occasions where I could celebrate without guilt. The same principles can be applied to my spiritual life. I have a range of spiritual practices that help to sustain me and I choose the appropriate ones for the day ahead. This will depend partly on where I am and what I am doing. For example, my priority during a time of convalescence was to look for God each day. Thus, all my journal entries contain a reflection on something that gave me insight into God. At the moment that is my five pieces of fruit or vegetable—the daily standard I try to keep to. I have also moved away from feeling guilty if there are some days when my engagement with God is more informal than formal, although my preference is to start the day with a quiet time. Thinking about what is spiritual healthy eating and whether I have been on an unhelpful diet is another way to look at a sustaining spirituality.

I have also moved away from feeling guilty if there are some days when my engagement with God is more informal than formal

Exercise and Personal Trainers

A personal trainer helps you work out and achieve your goals with your physical body; a spiritual director or similar can help you with your spiritual self. Many people find it easier to reflect on issues in partnership with others. Extraverts will often find out what they think when they speak it out loud. Working with someone else to encourage and develop your spirituality can be the added incentive to keep on going. In many areas of our lives when we know we are going to have to be accountable to someone it helps motivate us to keep going. Thinking more widely, which exercises do you focus on? Worship, Bible study, prayer, contemplation, meditation, service, prophecy, creativity, tongues…are there aspects of your spirituality that have been neglected and would merit a bit of a workout?

House

Thinking about your spirituality as a house can encourage reflection on what your foundations are, whether you have a good roof, what windows you look out of, which rooms you spend all your time in—rooms where you work or rest or play. What is growing in the garden? Who are the neighbours?

Wells

Paul has found the image of wells resonating recently. What wells do you drink from? Are there new wells to find? Old wells to revisit? Are there new depths to contemplate?

Where are you drinking from? Are you sustained by living water or have you been looking elsewhere for sustenance? Much of the rest of this booklet is about some of the wells we have discovered, dug or found discarded and cleared out for reuse.

Are you sustained by living water or have you been looking elsewhere for sustenance?

The important thing is to find an image or metaphor that works for you which may reflect your own interests, personality or tradition. Metaphors provide a structure for exploring spirituality and may open up new ways of thinking, talking about or developing your spirituality.

Is there a metaphor that you would find it helpful to use to explore your approach to sustaining spirituality?

3

Spiritual Exercises: The Examen and Discernment

Reflecting on what brings you life and death is the basic premise of the examen.

We like using the examen because it is helpful in understanding both the big picture and everyday life. It has played a significant part in Paul's life in particular. Here is his story:

> Like many journeys, I came to be ordained in a roundabout way. I was working for Youth for Christ while I was exploring my call to ordina-tion and initially I had never intended to be full-time in a parish. All through my curacy I wondered, 'What next?' The five years I spent as a curate in Aston were brilliant, I loved it. But I was challenged about whether I would actually enjoy leading a church. In the final year of my curacy I borrowed a book from my spiritual director, which introduced me to the idea of the examen. I read it every day for the whole of Lent that year and the process helped me to understand that being a Vicar would not bring me life, but that pursuing my one-day-a-week job with the Centre for Youth Ministry did. It helped clarify for me that even though I was extremely happy and fulfilled being a curate, the thought of working as a full-time leader of a church filled me horror! I ended up with two part-time jobs, one continuing lecturing in Youth Ministry and the other as a Chaplain at Birmingham Children's Hospital, where part of the attraction was to work with children and young people. I made the decision free from guilt and looking positively as to what really brought me life and not necessarily down the obvious path. This new ap-proach to discovering my ministry really challenged me at the time and some of my further reflections can be found in the web site resources.[8]

The examen is part of the 'Spiritual Exercises of Ignatius,' which were first published in 1548 but are still used by many today.[9] The examen is more fully called 'the examination of conscience or consciousness' or 'the awareness exa-men.' Through using the examen ourselves we are aware that there are three different areas that may be affected through using the process and where the insights might be applied. These are our relationship with God, our relation-ship to ourself or self awareness, and our relationship with others.

The premise of the examen is that we trust God the Holy Spirit to bring to mind those things which we need to focus on, work through, become aware of and so on. However, this can happen both when we are undertaking the process generally in reviewing a day, or more specifically around an area of concern. This latter element may include times, places, people, activities, roles, responsibilities, projects, critical incidents and so on.

A Basic Examen Process

1 It is probably best to keep a journal, some notes/record of your thoughts and observations. What will begin to emerge will be patterns, a flow, which will hopefully point out a consistency to what brings you life or death. Further insight comes the more often you do the exercise as you draw on different activities, experiences, days, weeks, moods and seasons.

2 Find a quiet place where you will not be distracted and reflect on your past day, week, month or other period. Allow at least 20 minutes for the process. It may take longer, depending on how far back in time you are going. If home does not provide sufficient peace and quiet, think about whether there is an outside space, an open church or somewhere else you can give this activity the time it needs. For some people, very late at night or early in the morning when no one else is around works best.

3 Ask yourself the questions below or other questions that seem helpful or relevant. Be honest with yourself and non-judgmental with what comes to mind. Do not sift out what you think is good or bad—try to just accept the thoughts. Jot them down and sit with them and see if they reflect you and your authentic feelings.

> - Where or when did you find consolation, joy, life or feel alive, re-charged, contented?
> - Where or when did you find desolation, death, draining, despair, frustration, sorrow?

4 Review the answers to the questions. What stands out to you? Where are the most powerful memories or feelings? What were you doing? Who were you with? Was there a single event that comes to mind when you ask the questions? What contexts are you exploring—relationship with God, self or others? Does anything surprise or concern you? Is there any action you need to take out of this reflection? Bear in mind here that Ignatius suggests that you should not change a previous decision when in a time of desolation. Thank God for the good things and ask for God's help in the difficult situations. If a need to forgive or ask for forgiveness emerges then work through that too.

5 As you do this over a few days, weeks, months, ask yourself:

- Do any patterns emerge?
- Are there any constants?
- Is any change being called for?
- What might this say about how you might best serve God?

We have found several benefits of using the examen. One is that it gives a structure around discernment and reflection. It can encourage the development of a discipline in doing this regularly rather than just in crisis or can provide a starting point for people who do not know where to begin in seeking to make a decision. The benefit of the examen is that we have to engage with both ways of seeing—we have to look at what brings both consolation and desolation—so for those who have a tendency to focus on one or other of these it helps bring a more rounded reflection.

The examen can be used in a variety of different ways and contexts such as:

- Putting a day to bed—dealing with feelings or experiences that you have not had an opportunity to process or which you are not aware need resolution until later.
- Dealing with an incident or experience that you are concerned about at a particular time.
- Providing a structure for reflective practice.
- Providing a holistic exploration of issues, that incorporates both consolation and desolation.
- As a tool and framework for dialogue in supervision or spiritual direction.
- Allowing the Holy Spirit to bring new insights and fresh perceptions.

I had a major operation that I had put off for several years. The interesting thing was that in doing the examen when I returned home, there were far more things in the experience that brought me life than brought me death and this helped me maintain a very positive attitude through the recuperation period.

The examen can help us to face up to problems or issues that we may not be fully aware of or are seeking to avoid. It can also act as a trigger to issues that are unresolved. A further way it is helpful is that the examen can bring elements of the subconscious and unconscious thoughts into a place where they are accessible, because we are asking questions and paying attention to feelings that may otherwise be ignored. Another facet of this is the idea of blind spots. The sign we might see on the back of a lorry which says 'If you can't see my mirrors I can't see you,' is helpful in making us aware of potential danger. Our blind spots can lead us into trouble if we are unaware of them and the examen can help uncover them. This is what Ignatius calls working with our dark side. In some ways the examen process can be seen as helping to acknowledge the power of what lies within and helping to process and work with and from that. However, what is uncovered and brought to the surface can be positive, and what is revealed by the Spirit through this process such as new paths, new insights, fresh perceptions, can surprise and enrich us.

Other reflective questions that may be helpful when exploring the wider panoramic landscape of vocation are:

- When do you most/least feel a sense of belonging/contributing?
- What do you most/least look forward to?
- What ideas, type of work or situation do you find you spend time thinking about or putting energy into even when you don't have to?
- Where or when has God blessed you in the past?
- What do you want people to be, do or discover?
- What is getting in the way of your being as effective as you would wish?
- What is in your life that supports and facilitates your being effective?
- When did you feel oppressed today?
- When did you feel most/least like yourself? Why?
- What were you doing when you most sensed you were doing what you were born for?

An example of this in practice is seen in Gregory's story. He was a youth worker in a very structured organization, which left little autonomy for him as a worker. After only a year in the job he was approached by another organization to apply for a job that on paper sounded a better fit for him. As we discussed the possibilities that this new job offered, Gregory realized that he would be exchanging one sort of death for another. He would lose some of the aspects he didn't like in his current job—being constrained by long-winded procedures and lack of understanding of what his profession offered—but gain management responsibilities that took him away from the face-to-face work that most motivated him. He stayed in his job. Exploring what brought desolation and consolation led to the right decision, even though an initial response would have been to move in the hope that things would be better. More information on the examen and vocation is available on the Grove web site.

Discernment

Reflecting on these or other relevant questions can be a great resource in sustaining ministry as they help you get to know yourself and your situation better, and bring a greater awareness of what God has called you to and how to work out that calling. When faced with a decision out of the examen process it is important to have some guidelines to help with the discernment process. Ignatius suggests a process, done over a period of time as follows:

Stage 1: Gather information from all relevant sources.

Stage 2: Frame the proposed change or decision clearly.

Stage 3: Look at the choice or decision in your mind's eye and see how you feel when you look at the different options stemming from it.

Stage 4: Weigh the advantages and disadvantages of the decision or choice.

Stage 5: Reflect on the particular choice or decision it seems to be right to make and offer it to God. Do you feel consolation or desolation? What advice would you give to someone else making a similar choice or decision? How does it feel in your head and in your heart? Take time over this stage if possible to let the decision or choice take root and for all the elements involved to become clear.

Questions you can use on such occasions include:

- Is it in harmony with your understanding of the Bible?
- Is it coherent with your values?
- Does it help you to be authentically you?
- Does it build the kingdom of God?
- Do you have an inner peace that goes beyond 'if it feels good, do it!'?
- Will it bring life?
- Can you make the decision with integrity?

Adopting a reflective approach to life can save us from making some mistakes, help us to deal with things that hold us back, develop our self-awareness and enable us to feel more sure of who we are and what God has called us to. Early in our ministries we were challenged as young leaders to consider whether we were 'called' or 'driven' as ministers. These tools have helped sustain our spirituality because they remind us of our calling and make us more consistently aware of the spiritual dimension of our lives.

Marker Posts and Shelters 4

> Nearly everyone senses that work alone is not sufficient for human fulfilment. One of the sad ironies of this situation is that, despite our intentions to allow a different quality of time in our lives, we often end up turning all our time into work time...The rhythm of life for countless people set up by this culturally pressured way, thus emerges as one that oscillates between driven achievement (both on and off the job) and some form of mind-numbing private escape.[10]

Life doesn't have to be like that—Jesus came to bring us life in all its fullness (John 10:10).

Originally we explored our response to this in relation to the idea of a rhythm and rule of life basing this on reading around monastic traditions. The idea of a rule of life has a long history—in many respects the Old Testament presents us with what was a Jewish rule and rhythm of life. The word 'rule' has a bad press today and we generally think about rules in terms of keeping and breaking them. However, the word rule in this context does not have the legalistic meaning we give it today. The words it comes from—Greek *canon* and Latin *regula*—are more about measurement, as in the word 'ruler.' It is something to measure ourselves against. Thinking further about this we have found the image of marker posts and shelters helpful. If you have ever walked the Pilgrim's Way across to Holy Island in Northumbria, you will have followed the marker posts which keep you on the right track. There are also shelters at regular intervals, which give protection should you get cut off when the tide comes in (or which you can use intentionally if you let the coastguard know in advance) but which also give a great view across the coastline. It is helpful to think about what marker posts and shelters we need in our lives to keep our destination in sight, to keep us safe and to help us on our pilgrimage.

If we look at the pattern of our lives we will see that there are rhythms involved. There are some things, which happen every day, week and so on, and there are seasons in life and ministry. It is important to see our lives in these periods as well. We have found that working out a realistic rhythm of life has been one of the foundations in sustaining our ministries. It has enabled us to find ways of giving ourselves fully to ministry but in such a way that this is sustainable, rather than overpowering or all encompassing, and we do feel we have a life as well. For us, weekends away at regular intervals are shelters—they are always there on the horizon, so we know that a safe place is in sight and can keep on going. Marker posts have been established in many of the areas we have listed below. These help us know where we are aiming in these different areas, give us boundaries to work within and help establish agreed priorities that help us shape the pattern of our days, weeks, months and years.

It is important that we work this out in line with our values, personality, calling and circumstances. Each of us is a unique individual and we all need to discover what works best for us. Earlier in this booklet I encouraged you to reflect on your calling and vocation, your vision for ministry. Having marker posts and shelters or a rule and rhythm of life helps achieve that. Every day we face choices and sometimes it is easiest to choose to respond to the most urgent things, which can mean that the most important get left behind. Having a thought-through structure to help us see the bigger picture can help us stay on track. Not everyone has a regular lifestyle with similar patterns for days, weeks, or months. Some may have personal circumstances that make it difficult to implement many of the suggestions in this book. However, even starting by putting in one or two marker posts or shelters may be helpful in the short term. For example, lighting a candle and looking at it for five minutes before you go to bed could help you quiet your mind and offer up to God the busyness of the day and the concerns of tomorrow.

Our experience is that we are more at peace with ourselves if our lives are an outworking of and a reflection of our values. Giving some time to identifying and reflecting on these and how our lives may be lived more consistently with them is well worth doing.

Establishing Your Shelters and Marker Posts or Developing Your Own Rhythm and Rule[11]

We use five headings for our rhythm of life-relationships, rest and recreation, youth work and service, stewardship, work and home life. Below we have listed some of the areas we consider under each of the sections. Try to develop a pattern that is something you can live with—do not be over-ambitious and try to be holistic. A rhythm of life should be a guide (not a constraint) and liberating (not oppressing). Our experience is that the spirit is willing but the flesh is weak when it comes to issues like this, but we have persevered and have seen some benefits in making sure that we have a holistic approach to life.

Values
Beginning by identifying your values can help you shape your pattern. What values underpin your life? Reflect on your past, your faith community, biblical or theological concepts that are important to you. What is important to

you and needs to be reflected in the shelters and marker posts or what theme may run through them all? We have put some of ours in the chart at the end of this chapter.

Relationships — consider:

- Relationship with God—what helps this to flourish?
- Relationships with the body of Christ—where and how does church happen for you?
- Relationships with your family—both immediate and wider family, using as broad a definition of family as is necessary. Roles as parent, child, spouse and so on have particular responsibilities and need time and prioritizing.
- Relationships with friends—who are you committed to and at what level? Where do friends fit into the daily, weekly, monthly or seasonal pattern?
- Accountability and support—who do you need in your life to help you be effective in your ministry? Who can you offer this to? We both have spiritual directors and offer this service to others.
- Biblical principles in relationships—the Old Testament injunction to remember the widow, alien and orphan, for example. What biblical principles are important to you that you want to include when you consider your relationships?

Rest and Recreation — consider:

- Space—for self, to do nothing, just to be, to reflect, to contemplate.
- Celebration—where does this fit? How can this be a regular part of life? What is happening that can be celebrated? Who needs joy bringing to their life? What memories can be created?
- Hobbies—recharge, do something different.
- Time off—the biblical principle of the Sabbath, which is often not Sunday for many people heavily involved in ministry. Our Sabbath is a Saturday and as far as possible we don't do any 'work' (including housework!) on that day and spend it doing what we enjoy.
- Holidays—times of fun and enjoyment, not necessarily going away but proper spaces away from work and ministry.
- Shared leisure—who can we include in our rest and recreation? Who might enjoy a day out or whose children can we entertain?
- Creativity—reflect our creative God—cook a special meal, write a poem.

Youth Work and Service — consider:

- What God has called you to and how this is worked out.
- Your formal and informal commitments as a youth worker.
- Study and developing your knowledge, skills and understanding.
- For those in full-time ministry, what you do for service outside of 'work.'
- Accountability.
- Investing in others.
- Your longer-term vocation and vision.

Stewardship — consider:

- Principles, for example, buying fairly traded items.
- Financial issues like giving, saving and spending.
- Possessions — do you own them or do they own you?
- Gifts and abilities — vocation, service, how do you use what God has given you?
- Time — what are your priorities? How do you manage your time effectively?
- Creation — being environmentally friendly. Do you take time to appreciate and enjoy what God has made? What can you do to protect God's creation?

Work and Home Life — consider:

- Planning — on a daily, weekly, monthly, seasonal and long-term basis, including time for vision-building.
- Those you live with, your neighbours and local community — what are your commitments to these different groups?
- Rhythm of work — high energy and low energy times — time with people, time alone. Working out when you are at your best and prioritizing in conjunction with this.
- Making a sacred space at home.
- Reflection time to enable you to develop your practice.
- Personal development — what new opportunities might be good to explore, including further training?

Use the grid to begin the process of identifying marker posts and shelters that can be a resource in sustaining you personally, spiritually and vocationally. We have made some suggestions in the boxes to help stimulate thinking.

My Marker Posts and Shelters[12]

Values:
Seeing God in the everyday, integrity, serving in our church and wherever God leads, offering spiritual support to others, having a sacred space at home, tithing, making sure retreat time and holidays are in the diary at the beginning of the year, longevity in ministry, God's bias to the poor…

Area	Daily	Weekly	Monthly	Annually	Seasonally
Relationships with God, others and myself	Connect with God Read Bible passage Text or email a friend	Ring family Journal Do examen Time of intercession or soaking prayer	See prayer partner Contact someone I don't see regularly Meet mentor or mentee	Retreat Visit friends who have moved away	See spiritual director Offer support to others Do something for Lent
Rest and recreation, relax and recharge	Get enough sleep! Unwind for at least 15 minutes	Go for a long walk Read the Sunday papers Have a Sabbath day	Have someone round for a meal	Do something special on birthdays and anniversaries Two week holiday	Celebrate festivals or other special events Weekend away
Youth work/ service	Pray for the young people	Watch/listen to something that keeps me in touch with youth culture	Read a relevant magazine Follow up a young person I haven't seen for a while	Go to a conference for some input	Get some supervision Review and plan the work
Stewardship	Use fairly traded tea and coffee	Recycle papers etc Walk somewhere instead of using the car	Sponsor a child Give to my church	Review lifestyle and commitments	Grow my own veg Make my own cards
Work and home life	Look for God in the everyday Pay someone a compliment	Do a small act of kindness for someone	Plan diary for the next month	Spring clean Organize carol singing	Review work/life balance

5

In this booklet I have sought to present some concepts and practices that are helpful in developing a personal spirituality that sustains in the long term, that helps through the hard times as well as the good times.

We came to some of these things quite late in our Christian journeys and wish that they had been introduced to us when we first became Christians. Being willing to explore outside our own traditions and comfort zones and having a more holistic approach to spirituality has enriched our lives and realizing that there are lots of ways and places to encounter God is very liberating.

Realizing that there are lots of ways and places to encounter God is very liberating

I hope that this is not a booklet to read once and discard. The topics in it would benefit from further study and reflection to see how some of these principles can be contextualized in your own life. There is also material in here which may be good to use with the young people you work with. For example, it may be helpful to use the mixer desk idea to help young people discern the different sounds in their lives and to develop a sound that is authentic for them. The two core examen questions could also be used by young people to reflect on their daily life, to try to put the day or week to bed and to give over to God the things that have been getting to them and praise him for what has been good. The discernment questions can help them evaluate decisions they are looking to make. Most of this material can be adapted to use with non-Christian young people too. The principles work outside of a faith context, in trying to build a more holistic lifestyle.

Some Closing Thoughts

- Give time to the process of exploring how your spirituality can be sustained.
- Seek out safe places and people who can accompany you on the

journey.
- Find sacred spaces where you can encounter God.
- Work out priorities and do not feel guilty if for a season you or your family are a priority.
- Identify what nourishes you and give time to that and do not worry if it seems odd or old fashioned.
- Do not worry about what others think, it is what God thinks that counts.
- See what baggage you are carrying that can be left behind.
- Be reflective and discerning and begin to make changes, even if they are only very small ones to begin with.
- Try consciously to look for God as you go about your everyday life.

Questions for Reflection

'I came that they may have life and have it abundantly.' (John 10:10)

- What does this mean for you?
- Does your personal spirituality help you live an abundant life?
- If not, what changes do you need to make?

Suggestions for further reading may be found on the web site.

Notes

1   www.sacredspace.ie

2   There is not the scope within this booklet to discuss this topic in depth. One useful resource is J Monbourquette, *How to Discover Your Personal Mission* (London: Darton, Longman and Todd, 2001).

3   See D Linn, M Linn and S Fabricant Linn *Sleeping with Bread* (Mahwah: Paulist Press, 1995) p 21 for a more detailed explanation of the concept.

4   We came across this concept in P Martin, 'Being Happy is Child's Play' *Sunday Times News Review* 6 February 2005.

5   H Nouwen, *Bread for the Journey* (London: Darton, Longman and Todd, 1996) p 12.

6   N Helm and P Allin, *Finding Support in Ministry* (Grove Pastoral booklet P 90) contains useful material.

7   S Nash, *Supporting Urban Youth Workers* (unpublished thesis, University of Sheffield/Urban Theology Unit, 2002).

8   The Grove web site www.grovebooks.co.uk has a section containing additional resources for this booklet and others.

9   See M Hebblethwaite, *Way of St Ignatius — Finding God in all things* (London: Fount, 1999) for further details.

10 Edwards cited in BE Eanes et al (eds), *What Brings You Life?* (Mahwah: Paulist Press, 2001) p 85.

11 H Miller, *Finding a Personal Rule of Life* (Grove Spirituality booklet S 8) gives a more detailed account of a rule of life.

12 There is a blank grid on the website to download and use.

NATALIA

C000171787

TI HO SPOSATO
PER ALLEGRIA *Joy /Fun*

COMMEDIA IN TRE ATTI

EDIZIONE SEMPLIFICATA AD USO
SCOLASTICO E AUTODIDATTICO

Questa edizione, il cui vocabolario è composto
con le parole italiane più usate, è stata abbre-
viata e semplificata per soddisfare le esigenze
degli studenti di un livello leggermente
avanzato.

Seguendo il metodo del DIZIONARIO GAR-
ZANTI DELLA LINGUA ITALIANA indi-
chiamo l'accento (.) sotto le parole non piane
e sotto quelle piane di tipo figlio, vecchio,
braccio, Vittoria e allegria, fotografia. Nelle
forme verbali finite l'accento è però riportato
soltanto all'imperativo in composizione con i
pronomi.

A CURA DI
Solveig Odland Danimarca

CONSULENTE
Ettore Lolli Danimarca
Frank King Inghilterra

Illustrazioni: Per Illum

Easy Readers

EGMONT

Stampato in Danimarca

NATALIA GINZBURG,

nata a Palermo 1916, trascorse l'infanzia e la giovinezza a Torino. Sposata a Leone Ginzburg, dirigente del movimento antifascista clandestino, lo seguì da 1940 al 1943 al confino a Pizzoli, un paesino in Abruzzo. In quel periodo scrisse il suo primo libro »La strada che va in città«. Nel 1943 la famiglia Ginzburg è a Roma ove Leone viene arrestato dai tedeschi e muore in carcere l'anno dopo.

Il mondo narrativo della scrittrice è popolato di piccoli personaggi e fatti della vita quotidiana. Il segreto dell'arte della Ginzburg è la semplicità, non espressione di superficialità, ma, al contrario di profonda analisi dell'ambiente descritto e di perfetto dominio dei mezzi espressivi.

La Ginzburg ha scritto racconti, romanzi, saggi e nel 1966 ha provato la via del teatro con »Ti ho sposato per allegria«. Alcune delle sue opere più note sono: »Tutti i nostri ieri« (1952), »Valentino«, racconti, (1957), »Le voci della sera« (1961), »Le piccole virtù«, saggi, (1962). Con »Lessico famigliare« (1963) vince il Premio Strega. Ultimamente ha pubblicato »Caro Michele« (1973).

cappello

ATTO PRIMO

PIETRO: Il mio *cappello,* dov'è?

GIULIANA: Hai un cappello?

PIETRO: L'avevo. Adesso non lo trovo più.

GIULIANA: Io non me lo ricordo questo cappello.

PIETRO: Forse non te lo puoi ricordare. Non lo metto da molto tempo. È solo un mese che ci conosciamo.

GIULIANA: Non dire così, »un mese che ci conosciamo«, come se io non fossi tua moglie.

PIETRO: Sei mia moglie da una settimana. In questa settimana non ho mai *messo* il cappello. Lo metto solo quando *piove* forte, e quando vado ai *funerali.* Oggi piove e devo andare a un funerale con mia madre.

GIULIANA: Vai a un funerale? Chi è *morto?*

PIETRO: È morto uno che si chiamava Lamberto Genova. Era un mio amico.

GIULIANA: Lamberto Genova? io lo conoscevo. Lo conoscevo *benissimo.* È morto?

PIETRO: Sì.

GIULIANA: Lamberto Genova. Io lo conoscevo, ti dico: Era molto innamorato di me.

---

messo, da mettere.
piove, funerale, vedi illustrazione pag. 6.
morto, da morire.
benissimo, molto bene.

piove

funerale

PIETRO: Vittoria! Guardi se riesce a trovare il mio cappello.

GIULIANA: Lo sai quando l'ho *visto* l'ultima volta?

PIETRO: Ma tu forse non l'hai mai visto!

GIULIANA: Non dicevo del cappello. Dicevo di Lamberto Genova. Lo sai quando è stato che l'ho visto per l'ultima volta?

PIETRO: Quando?

GIULIANA: Pochi giorni prima d'incontrarti. Gennaio, era. Pioveva e io me ne andavo in giro per le strade e avevo una grande voglia di morire.

VITTORIA: (entrando) Ecco il suo cappello. (Via)

---

visto, da vedere.

6

GIULIANA: Allora lo vedo, Lamberto Genova, venire avanti, piccolo, piccolo.

PIETRO: No. Il tuo Lamberto Genova non era quello che conoscevo io.

GIULIANA: Perché, quello che conoscevi tu non era piccolo?

PIETRO: No.

GIULIANA: Il mio invece era piccolo, coi capelli tutti bianchi . . . Allora, quella mattina, ho pensato appena l'ho visto: »speriamo che mi inviti a *pranzo*«. Infatti mi ha portato a pranzo. E intanto che mangiavo pensavo: »Questo qui è molto innamorato di me, e io magari me lo sposo, e sto tranquilla con lui, tanto buono, sarà come un padre per me«. Così pensavo.

PIETRO: Il mio Lamberto Genova aveva moglie e figli.

GIULIANA: Anche il mio aveva moglie e figli. Ma forse era pronto a *divorziare*. Era tanto innamorato di me.

PIETRO: E poi? dopo il pranzo?

GIULIANA: Poi niente. Mi ha accompagnato a casa con la sua macchina. Mi ha *promesso* di trovarmi un lavoro.

PIETRO: Il mio Lamberto Genova era una per-

---

pranzo, quello che si mangia all'una.
divorziare, non essere più marito e moglie.
promesso, da promettere.

sona molto seria, insomma, non era quello che dici tu. Adesso devo andarmene, perché mia madre mi aspetta.

GIULIANA: Che *allegria,* andare a un funerale con tua madre!

PIETRO: Perché di mia madre parli sempre in quel modo?

GIULIANA: No, dicevo solo che allegria, andare a un funerale insieme con quella *allegrona* di tua madre.

PIETRO: Puoi lasciare in pace mia madre, per piacere?

GIULIANA: Non vuoi sapere se mi ha trovato un lavoro Lamberto Genova? Non ci sono andata, perché poi ho incontrato te. Ero pronta a sposare *chiunque,* hai capito, quando ti ho incontrato. Anche Lamberto Genova. Chiunque. Ero pronta a tutto.

PIETRO: Me l'hai *detto.*

GIULIANA: A tutto. Volevo uscire da quella situazione.

PIETRO: Capito.

GIULIANA: Così ti ho sposato. ANCHE per i soldi. Hai capito?

PIETRO: Sì.

GIULIANA: E tu mi hai sposato ANCHE per

---

allegria, quello che si prova quando ci si diverte.
allegrona, donna sempre piena di allegria.
chiunque, qualsiasi persona.
detto, da dire.

pietà. È vero che mi hai sposato anche per pietà?

PIETRO: Vero. (Esce)

GIULIANA: (gli grida dietro) Perciò il nostro *matrimonio* è una cosa niente *solida*!

VITTORIA: (entrando) Lei non si alza?

GIULIANA: Per adesso no.

VITTORIA: *L'avvocato* torna tardi?

GIULIANA: Non lo so. È andato a un funerale.

VITTORIA: È morto qualcuno?

GIULIANA: È morto uno che si chiamava Lamberto Genova. Lo conoscevo anch'io, ma forse quello che io conoscevo non si chiamava Lamberto, forse si chiamava Alberto, non mi ricordo bene . . . Io non *ho memoria* per i nomi. Hai memoria tu?

VITTORIA: Io sì. Mi sarebbe piaciuto studiare, ma ho dovuto andare a lavorare in campagna. Eravamo nove fratelli.

GIULIANA: Invece a me studiare non è mai piaciuto. Io volevo fare *l'attrice.* Così, a diciassette anni sono andata via di casa.

VITTORIA: E non c'è ritornata mai più?

GIULIANA: Ci ritorno ogni tanto, ma non spesso. Non vado d'accordo con mia madre.

---

pietà, quello che si prova per una persona che soffre.
matrimonio, col matrimonio si diventa marito e moglie.
solido, fermo e sicuro.
avvocato, può fare l'avvocato chi ha finito gli studi di legge.
avere memoria, ricordare bene.
attrice, Sophia Loren per esempio è un'attrice.

VITTORIA: Adesso che si è sposata, sarà contenta sua madre? Non è andata a farle conoscere l'avvocato?

GIULIANA: Ancora no. Le ho mandato dei soldi. Ma sai, ho una gran paura che li abbia messi da parte. Per me. Per il giorno che io ne abbia bisogno.

VITTORIA: Ha ragione sua madre. Io ascolto sempre mia madre. Io per mia madre potrei buttarmi nel fuoco.

GIULIANA: Dov'è casa tua?

VITTORIA: Casa mia è a Fara Sabina. Ma adesso mi lasci fare i lavori. Mi tiene qui a *chiacchierare*, e io poi mi trovo indietro.

GIULIANA: Non puoi stare ancora un poco? Sai, io non avevo mai avuto una donna di servizio. Tu sei la prima che ho.

VITTORIA: Non l'avevano, la donna di servizio, a casa sua da sua madre?

GIULIANA: Ma no! Mia madre vive in Romagna, in un paese che si chiama Pieve di Montesecco. Io sono *nata* lì. È una casa piccola e senza luce.

VITTORIA: Ma allora lei è una quasi come me! lei è una povera!

GIULIANA: Non avevamo niente di niente. Eravamo molto poveri, e mia madre ogni tanto andava

---

chiacchierare, parlare.
nato, da nascere.

a chiedere un po' di soldi a mio padre che stava con un'altra donna, e aveva, con questa donna, *un mucchio di* bambini. Così di soldi ne aveva pochi anche lui. Io, a diciassette anni sono andata via.

VITTORIA: E allora?

GIULIANA: Sono venuta qui a Roma, dalla mia amica Elena. Volevo diventare un'attrice. I primi tempi mi sentivo felice, perché non stavo più a Pieve di Montesecco, ma stavo invece a Roma, nella stanza che Elena aveva a Campo dei Fiori. Non sapevo come fare a diventare un'attrice, ma pensavo che bastava che io camminassi per la strada perché qualcuno mi fermasse e dicesse: Ma lei è proprio quella che io cerco per il mio film! Così non facevo niente, giravo per le strade e aspettavo, e *consumavo* i miei pochi soldi. Poi ho trovato un lavoro. Mi ha *preso* uno che aveva un *negozio* di *dischi,* uno che si chiamava Paoluccio. Era molto innamorato di me.

VITTORIA: E lei?

GIULIANA: Io no. Nel negozio dei dischi ho conosciuto una persona. Era uno che veniva sempre a sentire i dischi. Aveva una faccia *pallida,* con degli occhi neri, *tristi,* tristi. Non rideva mai. Poi mi

---

un mucchio di, molti.
consumare, finire a poco a poco.
preso, da prendere.
negozio, dischi, vedi illustrazione pag. 12.
pallido, quasi senza colore.
triste, non contento.

disco

negozio

sono innamorata di lui. Si chiamava Manolo. E la Elena mi diceva: No, no, non innamorarti di quello lì! Non mi piace! è così nero, così nero!

VITTORIA: E allora?

GIULIANA: Allora questo Manolo stava sempre nel negozio, ascoltava i dischi e guardava con i suoi occhi neri così tristi, così tristi. E poi una volta mi ha portato a casa sua, in Via Giulia. Stava solo con un gatto.

VITTORIA: Nero?

GIULIANA: Bianco. Un gatto bianco, molto grosso. Non abbiamo mica *fatto* l'amore quella volta. È *rimasto* là col gatto in braccio, a sentire i dischi e a guardarmi con quel suo viso così triste ... Siamo

---

fatto, da fare.
rimasto, da rimanere.

andati avanti così per un poco. Io lo andavo a
trovare la sera, lo amavo e soffrivo. Ma lui mi diceva
che non poteva più amare. Perché pensava sempre
a sua moglie, che l'aveva lasciato. Sua moglie si
chiamava Topazia.

VITTORIA: E perché l'aveva lasciato?

GIULIANA: Perché era una donna che *si stancava*
subito degli uomini, e appena ne aveva uno ne
voleva subito un altro. Così lui mi ha detto. E mi
ha detto che ogni tanto questa Topazia ritornava
da lui, stanca e *disperata*, faceva il *bagno*, e poi di
nuovo andava via, in automobile. Cambiava sempre automobile.

stanza da bagno

---

stancarsi, diventare stanco.
disperato, molto triste.

VITTORIA: Che strane persone!

GIULIANA: Invece lui le automobili non le poteva soffrire. Era molto ricco ma i soldi non gli piacevano. Scriveva. Aveva scritto due libri. L'uno si chiamava: Portami via Gesù.

VITTORIA: Portami via Gesù?

GIULIANA: Ho provato a leggerlo. Ma non ci capivo una parola. L'ho *dato* anche a Elena, e anche lei non ci capiva niente. E sempre mi diceva: No, no, quello lì non mi piace. Non fa nemmeno l'amore, forse non può, forse non è un uomo.

VITTORIA: E poi? Aveva ragione la Elena?

GIULIANA: No. Poi Manolo mi ha detto di andare a stare da lui. La Elena era disperata, ma io non potevo dirgli di no, e allora, finalmente abbiamo fatto l'amore. E la mattina mi diceva di non alzarmi, che era inutile alzarsi. Così non sono più andata al negozio, e ho *perso* il posto.

VITTORIA: E lui diceva che adesso l'amava?

GIULIANA: No. Mi parlava sempre di sua moglie Topazia. Com'era bella, e come aveva *stile*. Io, invece, non avevo nessuno stile. E io mi sentivo *infelice*. Avevo perduto tutti i miei amici. La Elena non la vedevo quasi mai, e Paoluccio, quello del negozio dei dischi, anche lui non lo vedevo più.

dato, da dare.
perso, da perdere.
stile, particolare modo di essere.
infelice, non felice.

14

Stavo tutto il giorno a letto a pensare . . . Ero diventata un'altra persona. Qualche volta pensavo: »Chissà se mi sposerà?« Ma figurati se era il caso di chiederglielo. Non se ne parlava neanche. Non mi amava, ti dico. Mi trovava senza stile. Non gli andava bene niente delle cose che dicevo.

VITTORIA: Ma perché rimaneva con lui, se la trattava così?

GIULIANA: Perché non potevo andar via, non mi potevo muovere. E poi non è che mi trattasse male, qualche volta era buono con me, solo non aveva nessun interesse per me, nessuno . . . Erano più di tre mesi che stavo con lui, e mi sono *accorta* che aspettavo un bambino.

VITTORIA: Oh! E allora?

GIULIANA: E allora gliel'ho detto, e lui ha detto che mi sbagliavo, che non era possibile, e anch'io mi son messa a pensare che mi ero sbagliata. E una mattina, *mi sveglio,* e lui non c'è più. Trovo una lettera. Diceva che se ne andava per un poco. Diceva di non aspettarlo, perché non sapeva quando tornava.

VITTORIA: E lei? allora lei come ha fatto?

GIULIANA: Mi aveva lasciato un po' di soldi. Mica tanti. Trentamila lire.

VITTORIA: Poco.

---

accorto, da accorgere.
svegliarsi, non dormire più.

GIULIANA: Sì. Io ho cominciato a piangere, e ho pianto non so quanto tempo, senza mangiare e senza dormire. Non avevo nessuno con cui piangere, dovevo piangere sola. Non avevo nessun altro che il gatto. Infatti, Manolo non aveva portato via il gatto.

VITTORIA: E allora?

GIULIANA: Allora niente. A un bel momento sono uscita a comprare un po' da mangiare per il gatto e per me. Son passati degli altri giorni e io camminavo molto, giravo le strade sotto il sole, perché speravo che se mi stancavo, perdevo il bambino. Ma i giorni passavano e il bambino l'avevo sempre. Un giorno sento aprirsi la porta, e mi vedo davanti una ragazza *sporca*, con dei *calzoncini* bianchi, tutti sporchi. Mi guarda e io la guardo e le chiedo:

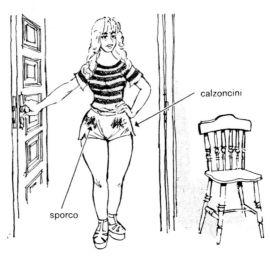

calzoncini

sporco

16

Scusi chi è lei? E la ragazza dice: Non c'è il signor
Manolo Pierfederici? E io dico: No, perché? Lei chi
è? e la ragazza dice: Io sono sua moglie. E io dico:
Topazia!

VITTORIA: Era Topazia!

GIULIANA: Sì. Se tu sapessi quanto ci avevo
pensato, a questa Topazia, quanto avevo cercato di
immaginarmela! Invece era così, una ragazza
sporca, con delle gambe grosse e gli occhi *celesti*. Mi
ha detto: Posso fare il bagno?

VITTORIA: E allora?

GIULIANA: E allora ha fatto il bagno, e dopo
si è seduta vicino a me e le ho raccontato tutto. A
un'altra, a quella Topazia che mi ero immaginata,
non avrei raccontato niente. Ma a questa qui avevo
voglia di raccontare tutto, come faccio adesso con
te. E le ho detto: Ma lei perché l'ha *piantato?* E lei ha
detto: Io l'ho piantato? È lui che ha piantato me.
Hai capito? Parlava così. Non aveva nessuno stile.

VITTORIA: Non aveva stile?

GIULIANA: Per niente. E mi ha detto: M'ha
piantato, poco dopo che eravamo sposati. Diceva
che non mi poteva amare. *Mi sono disperata,* ma poi
mi son trovata un lavoro. Faccio la *fotografa.* Giro

---

celeste, color del cielo.
piantare qlcu., lasciare qlcu.
disperarsi, diventare molto triste.
fotografo, chi fa fotografie per guadagnare soldi.

in automobile, e faccio delle fotografie per un *settimanale.* Qualche volta càpito qui. Siamo rimasti amici. Così ha detto Topazia, e io mi sentivo libera e contenta: in tutti quei mesi avevo pensato che lui non mi amava perché ero *stupida,* perché non avevo stile. L'ho detto a Topazia, e lei si è messa a ridere, e mi ha detto: Anche a te diceva che non avevi stile? me lo diceva sempre a me. Allora come ho *riso*! come abbiamo riso tutte e due!

VITTORIA: E poi?

GIULIANA: Poi abbiamo mangiato, e siamo andate a dormire. E prima di dormire Topazia mi ha detto: Domani pensiamo, col bambino, cosa puoi fare. Se vuoi tenerlo, ti aiuterò io, perché io non posso avere bambini. E io prima di dormire pensavo: »Sì, sì, lo tengo questo bambino! Lavorerò! Farò anch'io la fotografa!« Ma al mattino, quando mi sveglio, mi metto a piangere e dico: No, Topazia, no! io non mi sento di averlo questo bambino! Non ho casa, non ho lavoro, non ho soldi, non ho niente! e lei ha detto: Bene. E mi ha portato da un suo amico dottore e questo qui mi ha fatto *abortire.*

VITTORIA: E poi?

---

settimanale, giornale che esce una volta alla settimana.
stupido, che capisce poco.
riso, da ridere.
abortire, perdere il bambino prima che nasca.

GIULIANA: Poi sono stata qualche giorno a letto. Quando sono stata bene, andavo in giro con Topazia per la città. Faceva un mucchio di cose. Con lei come mi divertivo! Non avevo mai avuto un'amica, a parte la Elena. I momenti che stavo sola, pensavo qualcosa, e intanto mi dicevo: »Questa cosa che adesso ho pensato, bisogna che me la ricordo, perché tra poco viene Topazia e gliela racconto«. Io con Topazia stavo bene e mi sembrava tutto facile, con lei. E invece poi è tornata la Elena, e le ho raccontato tutto, e si è messa a piangere. Piange molto la Elena. Diceva: Lo sapevo! Lo sapevo che andava a finire così! E come farai con un bambino? E io dicevo: Ma se ho abortito! Lei diceva: Sì, hai abortito, va bene, ma un'altra volta che ti succede, come farai?

VITTORIA: E poi?

GIULIANA: Poi Topazia è partita. Doveva andare, per il suo lavoro, in America. Così io sono tornata a stare dalla Elena. Mi diceva che forse facevo bene a tornare a Pieve di Montesecco. Non avevo lavoro e giravo le strade e aspettavo che mi succedesse qualcosa.

VITTORIA: E allora?

GIULIANA: Allora poi un giorno ho incontrato un amico di Topazia, un fotografo, e mi ha portato a una festa. C'era un mucchio di gente e io non conoscevo nessuno. Però, dopo che ho bevuto un

sobria: sober

po' di vino, non mi sono più sentita sola. E lì, a quella festa, ho incontrato Pietro. Alla fine ero *ubriaca*, non trovavo più il fotografo, e *ballavo* sola con le *scarpe* in mano. Mi girava la testa, e sono

head spun

scarpa

ubriaco, che ha bevuto troppo vino.
ballare, muovere il corpo e i piedi secondo la musica.

tenere: to hold
≠ to have

Fitton O

/cadere
fell
caduta proprio vicino a Pietro. Non ho capito più niente, era il vino. E mi sono ritrovata in un letto. Pietro mi teneva la testa, e mi faceva bere del caffè. E poi mi ha accompagnato a casa. Lui è salito su con me.

VITTORIA: Su dalla Elena?

GIULIANA: Sì, ma la Elena in quei giorni non c'era, perché era dalla famiglia. Pietro è rimasto là. Gli ho raccontato tutto. Poi al mattino è andato. E io pensavo: non tornerà più. Invece dopo qualche ora è tornato con un mucchio di cose da mangiare. E abbiamo abitato insieme per dieci giorni, fino a quando è tornata la Elena. E in quei dieci giorni, io ogni tanto gli chiedevo: Trovi che ho stile? *every now & again* E lui diceva: No. Anche lui trovava che non avevo stile. Però, con lui, non me ne importava. Gli dicevo tutto quello che mi veniva in mente. E poi, quando stava per tornare la Elena, io gli ho detto: Sposami. Perché se non mi sposi tu, chi mi sposa?

VITTORIA: E lui?

GIULIANA: E lui ha detto: È vero. E m'ha sposata.

VITTORIA: Ma sa che lei ha avuto proprio una bella fortuna!

GIULIANA: Ancora non lo so se è stata una fortuna.

VITTORIA: Non è stata una fortuna? Sposarsi con un avvocato bello, giovane, con tanti soldi, lei povera?

GIULIANA: Già. Lavoro non ne avevo. E poi io

non ho tutta questa voglia di lavorare. Gli ho detto, a Pietro: Sì, ti sposo, però ho paura che non ti amo! con te non è come con Manolo! Quando è tornata a casa la Elena, le ho detto: Sai, ho trovato uno che mi sposa. E lei: Uno che ti sposa? Non voleva crederlo, che c'era uno che mi sposava.

VITTORIA: Dio, ma è tardi, devo mettermi a *cucinare*. Tra poco torna l'avvocato, e il pranzo non è pronto.

(Entra Pietro.)

PIETRO: Com'è che ancora non ha *rifatto* la stanza, Vittoria?

GIULIANA: Come faceva a rifare la stanza, non vedi che io sono a letto?

PIETRO: E non pensi di doverti alzare?

GIULIANA: Ho chiacchierato un po' con Vittoria. Le ho raccontato la mia vita. Stava a sentire, attenta attenta. Tu, invece, quando parlo, non mi ascolti. *Stamattina* sei uscito mentre stavo parlando. Eppure ti dicevo una cosa importante.

PIETRO: Ah sì? Cosa mi dicevi?

GIULIANA: Ti dicevo che non vedo, fra noi, una ragione seria di vivere insieme.

PIETRO: Mi dicevi questo?

GIULIANA: Sì.

---

cucinare, far da mangiare.
rifare, mettere in ordine.
stamattina, questa mattina.

PIETRO: Non abbiamo nessuna ragione seria di vivere insieme? Lo pensi?

GIULIANA: Lo penso. Trovo che sei una persona molto *leggera*.

PIETRO: Io non sono niente leggero. Io sono uno che sa sempre quello che fa.

GIULIANA: Hai un'alta *opinione* di te stesso!

PIETRO: Forse.

GIULIANA: Io invece non so mai quello che faccio. Del resto come fai a dire, che tu sai sempre quello che fai? Fin adesso non hai fatto niente. Niente d'importante, voglio dire. Sposarti è stata la prima cosa importante della tua vita.

PIETRO: Prima di incontrare te, sono stato sul punto di sposarmi almeno diciotto volte. Mi sono sempre tirato indietro. Perché scoprivo in quelle donne qualcosa che mi faceva paura. Scoprivo in loro un *pungiglione*. Erano delle *vespe*. Quando ho trovato te, che non sei una vespa, ti ho sposato.

GIULIANA: Non mi fa piacere sentire che non ho i pungiglioni. È vero, ma non mi piace.

vespa   pungiglione

---

leggero, qui: poco serio.
opinione, quello che si pensa di qualcuno o di qualcosa.

PIETRO: Se la verità non ti piace, vuol dire che sei ancora bambina. Bisogna accettare se stessi. Ma adesso devi alzarti e venire a mangiare.

GIULIANA: Sei molto sicuro di te e molto *antipatico*. Parli di me che mi sembra che tu mi *conosca come il fondo delle tue tasche*.

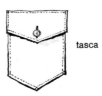

tasca

PIETRO: Infatti io ti conosco come il fondo delle mie tasche.

GIULIANA: Ci siamo incontrati che non è neanche un mese e mi conosci come il fondo delle tue tasche? Ma non sappiamo nemmeno perché ci siamo sposati! Non facciamo che domandarci perché, dalla mattina alla sera!

PIETRO: Tu. Io no. Io non mi domando niente. Tu sei una persona con le idee poco chiare. Io no. Io vedo chiaro. Vedo chiaro e lontano.

GIULIANA: Ma guarda che alta opinione che hai di te! »Vedo chiaro e lontano!« Io ti dico che non è vero, non vediamo chiaro niente!

PIETRO: Allora, lo fai il bagno?

GIULIANA: Eh?

---

antipatico, che non piace.
conoscere come il fondo delle sue tasche, conoscere molto bene.

PIETRO: Ti fa bene, *schiarisce* le idee.

GIULIANA: Non credo che farò il bagno. Sono troppo triste. Ho paura che tu sia troppo antipatico! (Va nel bagno. Tornando) Io trovo che il matrimonio è una cosa *orrenda*. Dover vivere insieme sempre, tutta la vita! Ma perché ti ho sposato? Ma cosa ho fatto? Dove avevo la testa quando ti ho preso?

PIETRO: Hai *deciso* di fare il bagno?

GIULIANA: Non hai detto che devo fare il bagno?

PIETRO: Non era mica un ordine.

GIULIANA: Lo credo bene. Vuoi anche cominciare a darmi degli ordini!

PIETRO: Allora mi trovi antipatico?

GIULIANA: Sì. Ho paura di sì. Sei così tranquillo, così sicuro di te! »Ti conosco come il fondo delle mie tasche!« »Vedo chiaro e lontano!« E se non mi conoscessi un bel niente? Se scopri in me un pungiglione? Se sono una vespa? allora? allora cosa faresti?

PIETRO: Ti pianterei. Si capisce.

GIULIANA: Non si capisce per nulla. Adesso mi hai sposato e mi tieni, mi tieni come sono! anche se sono tutta diversa da quello che credevi, devi tenermi lo stesso. Non ti dicevo che il matrimonio

---

schiarire, rendere chiaro.
orrendo, che fa paura.
deciso, da decidere.

25

è una cosa orrenda?

vittoria: (entrando) Non s'è ancora vestita? Io ho portato il pranzo in tavola!

pietro: Vieni a mangiare. Il bagno lo farai dopo.

giuliana: Già! se faccio il bagno dopo mangiato, muoio. Mi vuoi morta? (Va nel bagno.)

Domande

1. Da quanto sono sposati Pietro e Giuliana?

2. Perché Giuliana voleva sposarsi?

3. Perché Giuliana è andata via di casa?

4. Cambia in meglio la vita di Giuliana a Roma?

5. Quali persone Giuliana incontra a Roma?

6. Che tipo è Manolo? E come tratta le donne?

7. Che cosa racconta Manolo di Topazia?

8. Perché a Giuliana piace stare insieme a Topazia?

9. In che modo Giuliana incontra Pietro?

10. Che cosa pensano Giuliana e Pietro l'uno dell'altro? In che modo sono diversi?

11. Che opinione ha Giuliana del matrimonio?

ATTO SECONDO

PIETRO: Ho invitato a pranzo mia madre e mia sorella per domani.

GIULIANA: Ma tua madre non aveva detto che non avrebbe mai messo piede in questa casa?

PIETRO: L'aveva detto. Io però l'ho *convinta* a venire, domani, a pranzo. Dopo il funerale di Lamberto Genova, l'ho accompagnata a casa, e l'ho convinta. S'è lasciata convincere.

GIULIANA: Sei *mammone*, tu?

PIETRO: Non sono mammone, ma non voglio essere in guerra con mia madre. Preferisco essere in pace, se la cosa è possibile. Non andiamo a casa di mia madre, perché lì c'è la *zia* Filippa. La zia Filippa non ha voluto nemmeno guardare la tua fotografia. Mia madre sì, un momento, l'ha guardata.

GIULIANA: E cos'ha detto, della mia fotografia, tua madre?

PIETRO: Niente. Mia madre non ti piacerà. E tu non piacerai a lei. Niente le piacerà di questa casa. Nemmeno Vittoria.

GIULIANA: Perché non le deve piacere nemmeno Vittoria?

---

convinto, da convincere.
mammone, chi è troppo attaccato alla madre.
zia; sorella della madre o del padre.

PIETRO: Ha delle donne di servizio di un altro tipo.

GIULIANA: E allora se io non piacerò a lei, e se lei non piacerà a me, e se in questa casa niente le piacerà, perché la fai venire qui?

PIETRO: Perché è mia madre.

GIULIANA: Bella ragione. Io non ti porto mica qui mia madre, io. Sai come è mia madre? Mia madre tiene tutti i vecchi giornali sotto il letto, ne ha un mucchio, e le pagine e le fotografie che le piacciono le attacca sulle *pareti* e al capo del letto. Hai capito?

PIETRO: Sì. Va bene. Questa è tua madre. Mia madre è una donna abbastanza normale.

GIULIANA: Perché, vuoi dire che mia madre non è una donna normale? vuoi dire che è *matta?*

PIETRO: Non lo so. Da come ne parli tu, penso che un po' matta dev'essere. Io non l'ho mai vista.

GIULIANA: E ti sembra bello di non avere ancora visto mia madre?

PIETRO: Vuoi che andiamo a trovare tua madre?

GIULIANA: A vedere mia madre? a vedere i giornali sotto il letto?

PIETRO: Sì, perché no?

GIULIANA: Non è mica matta mia madre. È solo una povera donna.

---

parete, muro dentro la casa.
matto, che ha perso la ragione.

PIETRO: Ecco. E anche mia madre, vedi, è una povera vecchia donna.

GIULIANA: Perché, cosa le è *successo,* a tua madre?

PIETRO: Mia madre, da giovane, era bella e ha *sofferto* molto quando ha cominciato a *invecchiare.* Poi ha perduto un po' di soldi, non molti. E tante volte la mattina si sveglia e piange, perché ha paura di essere povera. Poi qualche anno fa è morto mio padre, e lei ne ha sofferto molto. Mia sorella non si è ancora sposata, e anche di questo lei piange. E adesso io mi sono sposato con te.

GIULIANA: Tua madre è invecchiata come invecchiamo tutti. Tuo padre è morto quando era già vecchio. Questo succede a tutti . . . Tua madre pensa che ti ho sposato per i soldi?

PIETRO: Sì, lo pensa. Pensa tutto, e la mattina si sveglia, e piange. Perciò le ho detto di venire qui a pranzo, così almeno ti vedrà in faccia.

GIULIANA: Certe cose che pensa tua madre sono vere. È vero che ti ho sposato ANCHE per i soldi.

PIETRO: Vorresti dire che non mi avresti sposato, se fossi stato povero?

GIULIANA: Non lo so! Non ho avuto il tempo di capirlo! Perché ci siamo sposati così presto?

PIETRO: Mi hai detto: Sposami! Se no, se non

---

successo, da succedere.
sofferto, da soffrire.
invecchiare, diventare vecchio.

mi sposi tu, chi mi sposa? se no finisce che mi butto dalla finestra. Non hai detto così?

GIULIANA: Sì, ho detto così. Ma era un modo di dire. Non era mica necessario sposarmi così presto. Forse abbiamo sbagliato a sposarci così presto, forse insieme saremo molto infelici!

PIETRO: È possibile.

GIULIANA: E allora? allora come faremo?

PIETRO: Divorzieremo.

GIULIANA: *All'estero?*

PIETRO: All'estero.

GIULIANA: Meno male che hai un po' di soldi, così almeno potremo andare all'estero a divorziare!

PIETRO: Meno male.

GIULIANA: Allora cosa devo fare da pranzo a tua madre?

PIETRO: Non so. *Pollo.* Mia madre sta poco bene.

GIULIANA: È molto vecchia, tua madre?

PIETRO: Vecchia, sì.

GIULIANA: Quanti anni ha?

PIETRO: Non si sa. Non lo sa nessuno.

GIULIANA: Quando saremo divorziati, cosa farai? tornerai a stare con tua madre, con tua sorella, e con la zia Filippa?

PIETRO: Forse.

GIULIANA: Io invece *viaggerò* con Topazia. Sai,

---

all'estero, in un altro Stato.
viaggiare, andare in viaggio.

tante volte mi chiedo cosa penserebbe Topazia di te. Ma non credo che le piaceresti. Direbbe che non hai stile. Topazia è molto difficile.

PIETRO: Però si è sposata con quello stupido.

GIULIANA: Manolo? perché dici così, »quello stupido«? Tu non lo conosci, Manolo!

PIETRO: Io penso che quel tuo Manolo era uno stupido, e un *vigliacco*. Non è andato via, quando ha saputo che aspettavi un figlio?

GIULIANA: Sì. Ma era un'altra cosa. Lui aveva paura della vita. Allora, per tua madre, pollo?

PIETRO: Pollo.

GIULIANA: Vittoria! Non risponde, forse chiacchiera con la ragazza del piano di sopra.

PIETRO: Cosa le vuoi dire?

GIULIANA: Che domani viene a pranzo tua madre.

PIETRO: E mia sorella.

GIULIANA: E tua sorella. Questa tua sorella com'è?

PIETRO: Mia sorella è un'*oca*.

GIULIANA: Le piacerò?

PIETRO: Le piacerai moltissimo.

pollo

oca

---

vigliacco, chi manca di coraggio.
oca, si dice di ragazza molto stupida.

GIULIANA: Perché è un'oca? Mi trovi fatta per piacere alle oche?

PIETRO: Non perché è un'oca. Perché è sempre contenta di tutto. È molto *ottimista*.

GIULIANA: Io sto bene con gli ottimisti.

PIETRO: E con me stai bene?

GIULIANA: Ancora non lo so. Ancora non ho capito bene come sei.

PIETRO: Io invece ti ho capita subito, appena ti ho vista.

GIULIANA: A quella festa? quando ballavo, ubriaca, senza le scarpe? Hai capito che ero una che ti andava benissimo a te?

PIETRO: Sì.

GIULIANA: Che bello.

PIETRO: E vuoi sapere una cosa?

GIULIANA: Cosa?

PIETRO: Non mi hai mai fatto nessuna pietà.

GIULIANA: Ma come? quella notte, quando piangevo, quando ti raccontavo, non ti facevo pietà?

PIETRO: No.

GIULIANA: Ma come, ero sola, senza soldi, senza lavoro, avevo anche abortito, e non ti facevo pietà?

PIETRO: No.

GIULIANA: Ma allora sei senza cuore!

PIETRO: Non essere stupida. Lo sai che io non

---

ottimista, chi vede soprattutto quello che è buono negli uomini e nelle cose.

ho mai sentito, guardandoti, nessuna pietà. Ho sempre sentito, guardandoti, una grande allegria. E non ti ho sposato perché mi facevi pietà. Ti ho sposato per allegria. Non lo sai, che ti ho sposato per allegria? Ma sì, lo sai benissimo.

GIULIANA: Mi hai sposato perché ti divertivi con me? E io? io perché ti ho sposato?

PIETRO: Per i soldi?

GIULIANA: ANCHE per i soldi.

PIETRO: Credo che uno si sposa sempre per una ragione sola. Gli ANCHE non valgono. C'è una ragione sola, ed è quella che importa. Non mi hai detto: Sposami, se no chi mi sposa?

GIULIANA: Sì, e allora?

PIETRO: Be', non era questa la ragione? che volevi avere un marito? Qualsiasi marito?

GIULIANA: Sì.

VITTORIA: (entrando) Mi ha chiamato?

GIULIANA: Non adesso. Prima. Volevo dirti che domani vengono a pranzo sua madre e sua sorella. Farai pollo.

VITTORIA: E c'è bisogno di dirmelo oggi?

GIULIANA: Sì, perché oggi che vai dal *parrucchiere*, lo compri.

VITTORIA: È vero, li vado sempre a comprare in Piazza Bologna, vicino al mio parrucchiere. Esco subito. (Via)

---

parrucchiere, chi fa i capelli alle donne.

PIETRO: Sembrerebbe una buona ragazza. Hai preso *informazioni,* prima di prenderla?

GIULIANA: Sì. Ho telefonato alla signora Giacchetta.

PIETRO: Chi è questa signora Giacchetta?

GIULIANA: È la signora Giacchetta. Quella dov'era prima. A Vittoria piaceva molto. Era molto brava in casa. Faceva tutto da sé. A lei, a Vittoria, non le lasciava nemmeno mettere le mani in acqua. Non capisco perché teneva la donna.

PIETRO: Sei sicura che esiste, questa signora Giacchetta?

GIULIANA: Se mi ha *risposto* quando le ho telefonato!

PIETRO: Non si prendono informazioni così, si va sul luogo.

GIULIANA: Di che cosa potremo parlare, domani, con tua madre? Dopo che avremo parlato un po' di Vittoria, di che cosa potremo parlare?

PIETRO: Ah, davvero non lo so!

GIULIANA: Possiamo parlare del Lamberto Genova?

PIETRO: Quale, del tuo o del mio?

GIULIANA: Un po' dell'uno, un po' dell'altro, no?

PIETRO: Devo uscire. Dov'è il mio cappello?

GIULIANA: Hai un altro funerale?

---

informazione, notizia.
risposto, da rispondere.

PIETRO: No. Piove. Quando piove, metto il cappello.

GIULIANA: Oh Dio, piove, e adesso Vittoria è dal parrucchiere ...

Domande

1. Perché Giuliana non piacerà alla madre di Pietro?

2. In che modo sono diverse le due madri?

3. Per quali ragioni ha sofferto la madre di Pietro?

4. In che modo Pietro è diverso da Manolo?

5. Perché Pietro si è sposato con Giuliana?

6. In quali casi Pietro porta il cappello?

3*

ATTO TERZO

GIULIANA: Pietro!

PIETRO: Eccomi.

GIULIANA: Vittoria non è tornata!

PIETRO: Come non è tornata?

GIULIANA: Non è tornata, da ieri, dopo il parrucchiere. Tu stavi fuori a mangiare ieri sera, io
me ne sono andata a dormire presto. Stamattina,
dopo che sei uscito tu, la chiamo, la cerco in tutta
la casa, e non c'è.

PIETRO: Dobbiamo telefonare alla polizia?

GIULIANA: No. La ragazza del piano di sopra
dice che forse è andata di nuovo dalla signora
Giacchetta. Le piaceva così tanto stare dalla signora
Giacchetta. Non aveva quasi niente da fare. Qui
anche le piaceva, ma trovava che c'era troppo
lavoro.

PIETRO: Che lavoro c'è, qui? Siamo due persone
sole, la casa è piccola? Come hai fatto per cucinare?
Tra poco, saranno qui mia sorella e mia madre.

GIULIANA: Mi sono alzata tardi, stamattina, e poi
speravo sempre che tornasse Vittoria. (Via)

(Pietro solo. Comincia a rifare la stanza. Suona il
campanello. Pietro va a aprire. Entrano la madre e
la sorella di Pietro.)

campanello

scale

GINESTRA: Oh, mamma, guarda che bellissima casa!

MADRE DI PIETRO: Troppe *scale*. Io soffro di cuore, e le scale mi fanno male.

GINESTRA: Tu non soffri di cuore, mamma. L'ha detto il dottore.

ipocondriaca

MADRE DI PIETRO: L'hanno detto anche a Lamberto Gẹnova, che non soffriva di cuore pochi giorni prima che morisse. Me l'ha detto la povera Virginia.

PIETRO: Perché la chiami povera Virginia? Non è mica morta anche lei?

MADRE DI PIETRO: Povera Virginia! Non è morta, ma è rimasta sola, e quasi senza soldi!

(Entra Giuliana.)

MADRE DI PIETRO: Buongiorno, signorina.

GINESTRA: Buongiorno.

GIULIANA: Buongiorno.

GINESTRA: Che bella casa che avete!

GIULIANA: Posso chiederle di non chiamarmi signorina, dato che ho sposato suo figlio una settimana fa.

MADRE DI PIETRO: Non vi siete sposati in chiesa. Per me vale solo il matrimonio in chiesa. Ad ogni modo, la chiamo signora, se vuole.

PIETRO: Non vorresti chiamarla per nome, mamma? Il suo nome è Giuliana.

MADRE DI PIETRO: Di dove è lei?

GIULIANA: Io sono di Pieve di Montesecco.

MADRE DI PIETRO: E dov'è questo Pieve di Montesecco?

GIULIANA: In Romagna.

MADRE DI PIETRO: Ah in Romagna? Anche Rossignano è in Romagna. Conosce Rossignano?

GIULIANA: No.

MADRE DI PIETRO: Non conosce Rossignano? È

strano. Non la portavano in *villeggiatura* a Rossignano, da bambina? Dove la portavano?

GIULIANA: Non mi portavano in villeggiatura.

MADRE DI PIETRO: Ah non la portavano?

GIULIANA: No. Mia madre non aveva denari. Mio padre, quando io ero piccola, è andato via di casa.

MADRE DI PIETRO: Anche io sono stata molto provata dalla vita. Ho perduto mio marito. E ora mio figlio ha voluto darmi questo grande *dolore*. Io non ho niente contro di lei, signorina, o signora o Giuliana, come vuole. Ma non credo che lei sia la moglie giusta per mio figlio. Sa perché mio figlio l'ha voluto?

GIULIANA: No?

MADRE DI PIETRO: Per darmi un dolore.

PIETRO: La nostra donna di servizio Vittoria, ieri è andata dal suo parrucchiere, e non è più ritornata.

MADRE DI PIETRO: Dovete guardare se non si è portata via qualche cosa.

GIULIANA: Vittoria? Oh no, Vittoria non toccava niente.

MADRE DI PIETRO: Da quanto l'avevate?

PIETRO: Quattro giorni.

MADRE DI PIETRO: Avevate preso informazioni, di questa Vittoria?

---

villeggiatura, luogo in campagna al mare o in montagna dove si
va a passare il tempo libero.
dolore, quello che si prova quando si soffre.

PIETRO: Sì. Dalla signora Giacchetta.

(Entra Vittoria.)

GIULIANA: Oh Vittoria! Finalmente sei ritornata. Avevo paura che non ritornassi più!

VITTORIA: Ieri sera, quando sono uscita dal parrucchiere, pioveva forte. Allora sono salita su un momento dalla signora Giacchetta. M'ha pregato di fermarmi a dormire, perché era sola, e aveva paura. Il marito era andato a Rieti. Stamattina è tornato il marito, e aveva portato quattro polli. Lei li ha cucinati e me ne ha dati due. Meno male che non hanno ancora mangiato. Mi ha accompagnato la signora Giacchetta con la macchina, per fare prima. (Via)

MADRE DI PIETRO: Sta fuori tutta la notte, e voi non dite niente?

GIULIANA: Sono così contenta che è tornata!

MADRE DI PIETRO: Non le dite niente? Non viene a casa perché piove. Ma in che mondo viviamo?

(Vittoria torna con i polli.)

MADRE DI PIETRO: Le donne di servizio, da Virginia, non ci vogliono stare. Non so perché. Quest'anno ne ha cambiate sei. Adesso ha soltanto una ragazza di quindici anni, non ha potuto trovare altro.

GINESTRA: Dicono che gli dà da mangiare poco.

MADRE DI PIETRO: Sì, è vero, Virginia non ha mai tenuto molto al mangiare, nemmeno per sé. Dice

40

che sono soldi buttati via. Così, quando è mancato il povero Lamberto, si trovava sola Virginia, sola in casa con quella bambina di quindici anni. Ha molto coraggio. Il povero Lamberto si è sentito male nella stanza da bagno. Lei con le sue braccia l'ha portato sul letto. È morto. La povera Virginia dovrà forse vendere la casa. Dice che vuole mettersi a lavorare. Ha molto coraggio. Io la vedo ogni giorno, le sto molto vicino, perché è sola. Passa le sere con quella ragazza, ma ora anche quella dice che vuole andarsene via.

PIETRO: Forse ha trovato un altro posto, dove spera di mangiare di più.

MADRE DI PIETRO: Sì, è possibile. Il povero Lamberto, qualche volta, me lo diceva che mangiavano poco a casa sua. La povera Virginia è già tanto *magra*.

PIETRO: È la donna più brutta che conosco.

MADRE DI PIETRO: Non è vero. Perché? Voi avete sempre bisogno di dir male di tutti. Non è brutta Virginia. Ha bellissimi capelli. E poi, veste bene. Ha moltissimo stile.

GIULIANA: Ha molto stile?

MADRE DI PIETRO: Moltissimo. E poi, si fa tutto da sé. Si fa dei *vestiti* a *maglia,* bellissimi. Ne ha fatto uno a Ginestra. Vero Ginestra?

---

magro, che pesa poco.
vestito, maglia, vedi illustrazione pag. 42.

GINESTRA: Però quello che ha fatto a me, la prima volta che l'ho lavato, è diventato lungo lungo. Non lo posso più portare.

MADRE DI PIETRO: Se lei vuole, Giuliana, figlia mia, dirò a Virginia di fare anche a lei un vestito.

GIULIANA: Penso che adesso abbia altro per la testa Virginia, che farmi un vestito.

MADRE DI PIETRO: No. Lo farà con grande piacere. Io vado a trovarla anche oggi, quando esco di qua. Lamberto Genova era un amico carissimo della nostra famiglia. Morire così! Dio ha voluto darmi anche questo grande dolore. Prima quel dolore che mi ha dato mio figlio sposandosi così, senza nemmeno avermi spiegato bene con chi si sposa! E non in chiesa. Allora il povero Lamberto è venuto a trovarmi, poche sere prima di morire. Mi ha detto: Stai molto vicina a Virginia, quando io non ci sarò più. Io gli ho detto: Lamberto mio, col mio cuore in questo stato, e tanti dolori, me ne andrò molto prima di te. Mi ha detto: Stai attenta al tuo cuore. È un cuore che ha sofferto. Non

vestito   maglia

bisogna darsi pena per i figli. I figli vanno per la loro strada. Io gli ho detto: Lamberto mio, ma fare un matrimonio così. Non ho niente contro di lei, signorina. Deve capirmi, sono madre, un giorno sarà madre anche lei. Mi hanno detto che vi siete incontrati a una festa. E a questa festa lei si è sentita poco bene, vero?

GIULIANA: Avevo bevuto troppo.

MADRE DI PIETRO: Vino?

GIULIANA: Vino rosso.

MADRE DI PIETRO: Si vede che era vino *cattivo*. La gente ora dà le feste col vino cattivo. Un'altra volta, quando va a qualche festa, non beva. Beva solo acqua. Le conosceva bene quelle persone?

GIULIANA: No. Io non conoscevo nessuno. Sono capitata là per caso, con un fotografo, che era amico della mia amica Topazia.

MADRE DI PIETRO: Li conoscevi bene, tu, Pietro?

PIETRO: Non li conoscevo per niente. Anch'io ci sono capitato per caso.

MADRE DI PIETRO: Hai bevuto anche tu?

PIETRO: Ho bevuto un poco.

MADRE DI PIETRO: Perché bevi nelle case che non conosci? Chi è questa sua amica Topazia?

GIULIANA: È una mia cara amica, Topazia, l'amica più cara che ho. È ottimista. Io sto bene con gli ottimisti.

---

cattivo, non buono.

MADRE DI PIETRO: E mio figlio? le sembra forse un ottimista, mio figlio?

GIULIANA: Credo di sì. Se no forse non l'avrei sposato.

MADRE DI PIETRO: Lo crede ottimista? Sbaglia. Perché non ha *riflettuto*, prima di sposarsi, figlia mia? Non è *credente*, vero, signorina? Me lo immaginavo. Non è credente. Se fosse stata credente, avrebbe chiesto a Dio che la aiutasse, e non avrebbe sposato mio figlio. Eppure più la guardo, e più mi sembra d'averla già vista? dove? Questa amica Patrizia, o come ha detto che si chiama? chi è?

GIULIANA: Non Patrizia. Topazia.

GINESTRA: Non sarà Topazia Valcipriana?

MADRE DI PIETRO: Chi, Valcipriana? Ah, la ragazza Valcipriana, è vero, si chiama Topazia. Quella che ha sposato quel Pierfederici?

PIETRO: Portami via Gesù!

MADRE DI PIETRO: Sì, si chiama così uno dei suoi libri. Ma non parla niente di Gesù. È pieno di parole sporche. Questo Pierfederici era molto bello. Soprattutto, aveva molto stile. Lei, la ragazza Valcipriana, non è brutta, ma non ha stile.

GIULIANA: Trova che non ha stile?

MADRE DI PIETRO: Neanche un po'. Allora questo Pierfederici ha sposato la Valcipriana e l'ha lasciata

---

riflettere, pensare attentamente.
credente, che crede in Dio.

subito, dopo quattordici giorni di matrimonio. E questa ragazza anche lei è finita male. Non vuole più stare con i suoi. Viaggia. È piena di uomini. Pare che non possa avere bambini. È sua amica?

GIULIANA: Sì.

MADRE DI PIETRO: Ah, ma ecco lei dove l'ho vista! L'ho vista al caffè Aragno, con la Valcipriana. Con questa Topazia. La Valcipriana aveva dei calzoncini bianchi tutti sporchi, e pareva un ragazzo di strada. Lei aveva un vestito rosso. L'ha ancora, quel vestito rosso?

GIULIANA: Sì.

MADRE DI PIETRO: Non lo metta più, lo dia a Vittoria. È un vestito che non le sta bene. Ieri, al funerale del povero Lamberto, Pietro aveva in testa un orrendo cappello. Glielo faccia buttare via quel cappello.

PIETRO: Mai! È un cappello molto buono.

MADRE DI PIETRO: Allora domando a Virginia di farle un vestito. Vado ora da lei, così comincia subito. Di che colore lo vuole, il vestito?

GIULIANA: Forse verde?

MADRE DI PIETRO: Verde? verde chiaro? Ho paura che non le stia bene. Meglio verde-acqua. Andiamo Ginestra. (Si mette il cappello.)

PIETRO: Che bel cappello!

GINESTRA: La mamma, appena ha saputo che ti sposavi, è corsa subito a comprarsi quel cappello.

MADRE DI PIETRO: Sì. Perché credevo che vi sareste sposati in chiesa. Non potevo mica immaginare che avreste fatto le cose in quel modo. Per darmi un dolore. Andiamo, Ginestra.

GINESTRA: Arrivederci. Grazie.

PIETRO: Arrivederci.

GIULIANA: Arrivederci.

MADRE DI PIETRO: Arrivederci.

(Madre di Pietro e Ginestra via.

Giuliana e Pietro soli.)

GIULIANA: Ho paura che avrò quel vestito della povera Virginia. Questa tua madre è un poco *svaporata*. Non me l'avevi detto che era un poco svaporata. Come è diversa tua madre dalla mia! Abbiamo delle madri così diverse. Con delle madri così diverse, e tutto così diverso, potremo vivere insieme?

PIETRO: Non so. Staremo a vedere.

GIULIANA: Tua madre non pensa che ti ho sposato per i soldi. Non pensa niente, tua madre. È troppo svaporata per pensare.

PIETRO: Già.

GIULIANA: In fondo non le importa nemmeno molto di sapere bene da dove sono arrivata io.

PIETRO: Sì. È così.

GIULIANA: Ma perché le madri sono tanto impor-

---

svaporato, si può dire di persona che parla senza pensare.

tanti? Com'è strano! Queste madri che se ne stanno là, in fondo alla nostra vita, così importanti per noi! Quella tua madre così svaporata, eppure così importante. In fondo ci conosciamo così poco. Dovremmo cercare di capire bene come siamo. Se no, che matrimonio è?

PIETRO: Ah, adesso non cominciamo di nuovo a parlare del nostro matrimonio! Ci siamo sposati e basta. Dov'è il mio cappello?

GIULIANA: Hai un funerale?

PIETRO: No. E non piove. Ma voglio il mio cappello. Ho deciso di andare in giro sempre col cappello.

GIULIANA: Forse perché tua madre ha detto che quel cappello non lo può soffrire?

PIETRO: Forse.

GIULIANA: Vedi come sono importanti le madri?

PIETRO: Andremo a vedere anche tua madre.

GIULIANA: Però a un certo punto è anche giusto mandarle un poco al *diavolo,* no? Volergli bene

diavolo

47

magari, però mandarle un poco al diavolo. È vero?

PIETRO: Certo.

GIULIANA: Sai cosa penso?

PIETRO: Cosa?

GIULIANA: Penso che forse io questo Lamberto Genova non l'ho proprio mai conosciuto.

Domande

1. Perché non è tornata Vittoria?

2. Perché la madre non accetta il matrimonio di Pietro?

3. Esiste un solo Lamberto Genova?

4. Che cosa hanno in comune la madre di Pietro e Lamberto Genova?

5. Perché la madre di Pietro considera Virginia una donna di coraggio?

6. Come sono Topazia e Manolo secondo la madre di Pietro?

7. La madre come tenta di costringere Giuliana e Pietro a seguire la sua volontà?

8. Come cercano Giuliana e Pietro di difendere la loro libertà?

9. In che modo il cappello è importante per Pietro?

www.easyreaders.eu

EASY READERS *Danimarca*

ERNST KLETT SPRACHEN *Germania*

ARCOBALENO *Spagna*

LIBER *Svezia*

PRACTICUM EDUCATIEF BV. *Olanda*

EMC CORP. *Stati Uniti*

EUROPEAN SCHOOLBOOKS PUBLISHING LTD. *Inghilterra*

ITALIA SHOBO *Giappone*

ALLECTO LTD *Estonia*

Opere della letteratura italiana ridotte e semplificate
ad uso degli studenti.
Le strutture e i vocaboli di questa edizione sono tra i più
comuni della lingua italiana.
I vocaboli meno usuali o di più difficile comprensione
vengono spiegati per mezzo di disegni o note.
L'elenco delle opere già pubblicate è stampato all'interno
della copertina.
C'è sempre un EASY READER a Vostra disposizione per una
lettura piacevole e istruttiva.
Gli EASY READERS si trovano anche in tedesco, francese,
inglese, spagnolo e russo.

TITOLI GIÀ PUBBLICATI:

Per ragioni di diritto d'autore alcuni dei titoli summenzionati non sono in vendita in tutti i paisi. Si prega di consultare il catalogo dell'editore nazionale.